THE KING WHO STOPPED THE RIVER

Illustrations :
M. Mohandas

ONCE UPON A TIME THERE WAS A FOOLISH KING WHO HAD A WISE DIWAN. ONE WARM SUMMER NIGHT THE KING COULD NOT SLEEP.

IT MUST BE ALMOST ONE O'CLOCK.

BONG...

YES, THERE GOES THE GONG.

ONE HOUR LATER —

BONG...

THERE GOES ANOTHER GONG... IT'S TWO O'CLOCK.

AT LAST WHEN HE HEARD THE SIXTH GONG, THE KING SAT UP.

IT'S SIX O'CLOCK! I'LL HAVE TO GET UP NOW. BUT I FEEL SO DULL.

I THINK I'LL RIDE OUT INTO THE COUNTRYSIDE AND GET SOME FRESH AIR.

TELL THE DIWAN TO GET READY. WE WILL GO RIDING TODAY.

1

SO THE KING AND HIS WISE DIWAN SET OUT.

AN HOUR LATER —

YOUR MAJESTY, HOW DO YOU FEEL NOW?

MUCH BETTER.

BUT I'M THIRSTY. LET'S STOP BY THAT RIVER.

SUCH CLEAR, SPARKLING WATER! WHERE DOES THIS RIVER FLOW?

IT FLOWS DOWN TO THAT KINGDOM IN THE EAST, YOUR MAJESTY.

OUR RIVER FLOWING INTO THEIR COUNTRY?

WE MUST STOP IT AT ONCE.

BUT YOUR MAJESTY...

NO BUTS, DIWAN. I WANT A DAM BUILT HERE.

THE DAM WAS BUILT. BUT NOW SINCE THE RIVER COULD NOT FLOW DOWN ITS USUAL COURSE...

...IT OVERFLOWED ITS BANKS AND FLOODED THE COUNTRYSIDE.

IT WILL BE WORSE DURING THE MONSOON.

SO WHAT?

WE'VE GOT OUR RIVER ALL TO OUR-SELVES, HAVEN'T WE?

HOW FOOLISH CAN HE GET?

CAN'T HE SEE THAT OUR NEIGHBOURS WILL SOON ATTACK US FOR STOP-PING THEIR WATER SUPPLY?

I MUST GET HIM TO BREAK DOWN THAT DAM...

AH! I'VE GOT IT!

THAT EVENING THE DIWAN WENT UP TO THE TOWER FROM WHICH THE GONG WAS SOUNDED...

...AND SPOKE TO THE MAN THERE.

AFTER MIDNIGHT I WANT YOU TO SOUND THE GONG EVERY HALF-HOUR. NOT EVERY HOUR, AS YOU DO NOW.

AS YOU COMMAND, SIR.

BECAUSE OF THE DIWAN'S ORDER IT WAS ONLY 3 O'CLOCK WHEN THE SIXTH GONG WAS SOUNDED.

BONG

BONG-ooo

ZZZZZ

THE SIXTH GONG! IT'S SIX O'CLOCK. I'D BETTER WAKE UP THE OTHERS.

GET UP! OUR DUTY IS OVER...

ZZZHUH!

IS IT SIX O'CLOCK ALREADY?

IT IS.

IT'S SIX O'CLOCK BUT THE SUN HASN'T RISEN AS YET.

HASN'T RISEN? WHAT DO YOU MEAN THE SUN HASN'T RISEN?!

IT HASN'T, YOUR MAJESTY. SEE FOR YOURSELF.

YOU'RE RIGHT.

SUMMON THE DIWAN!

WHEN THE DIWAN CAME —

WHAT'S ALL THIS! WHY HASN'T THE SUN COME UP AS YET?

I HAVE BEEN THINKING ABOUT IT, YOUR MAJESTY.

THERE CAN BE ONLY ONE REASON.

WHAT?

6

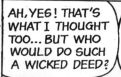

SOMEBODY HAS CAUGHT THE SUN AND IS NOT LETTING IT COME OVER OUR LAND.

CAUGHT THE SUN?

AH, YES! THAT'S WHAT I THOUGHT TOO... BUT WHO WOULD DO SUCH A WICKED DEED?

IT MUST BE THE KING OF THE EASTERN KINGDOM, WHO ELSE?

I HEARD HE WAS ANGRY BECAUSE WE STOPPED THE RIVER FROM FLOWING INTO HIS COUNTRY.

OH!

AND AS YOU KNOW, THE SUN PASSES OVER HIS KINGDOM BEFORE IT COMES OVER OURS.

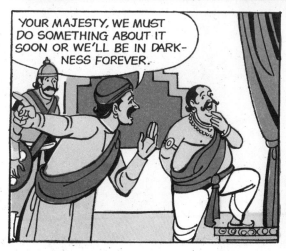

YOUR MAJESTY, WE MUST DO SOMETHING ABOUT IT SOON OR WE'LL BE IN DARKNESS FOREVER.

DO YOU THINK...

YES?

DO YOU THINK HE WOULD LET THE SUN GO IF WE LET THE RIVER FLOW INTO HIS COUNTRY AGAIN?

WHAT A BRILLIANT IDEA, YOUR MAJESTY!

AH, WELL, MY MOTHER ALWAYS SAID I WAS A VERY CLEVER FELLOW!

WELL, NOW... WE'LL HAVE TO BREAK DOWN THAT DAM.

I AGREE.

SUMMON THE COMMANDER OF MY ARMY!

I AM HERE, YOUR MAJESTY.

GET YOUR MEN! WE ARE GOING DOWN TO THE RIVER TO PULL DOWN THAT DAM AS FAST AS WE CAN.

THE KING LED HIS MEN TO THE RIVER...

8

...AND BEFORE DAWN THEY BROKE THE DAM DOWN.

THE RIVER BEGAN TO FLOW TO THE NEIGHBOURING COUNTRY AGAIN.

THE SUN SHOULD BE COMING UP ANY MOMENT NOW.

AND SURE ENOUGH —

THE SUN! LOOK! THEY'VE LET THE SUN GO!

YOUR PLAN WORKED, YOUR MAJESTY.

YOU HAVE SAVED THE COUNTRY.

OH, IT WAS NOTHING...

THE KING NEVER REALISED HOW HE HAD BEEN FOOLED BY THE DIWAN.

PUNYAKOTI
- A folktale from Karnataka.

Script:

Illustrations:
K. Chandranath

HULIA THE TIGER WAS WEAK WITH HUNGER.

HE HAD NOT EATEN ANYTHING FOR DAYS.

IF I DON'T FIND SOME FOOD TODAY, I'LL DIE OF HUNGER.

JUST THEN—

TIN-TIN

WHAT'S THAT?

THE CATTLE RETURNING HOME AFTER GRAZING!

WHAT'S WRONG WITH ME? I COULDN'T CATCH A SILLY COW!

WHO DO I SEE COMING THIS WAY?

IT WAS A COW CALLED PUNYAKOTI.

I'D BETTER WALK FASTER. MY CHILD MUST BE WAITING FOR ME.

EH!

YES, I'VE BEEN WAITING FOR YOU.

HULIA, PLEASE LISTEN...

NO! I WON'T!

I AM GOING TO KILL YOU AND EAT YOU UP.

KILL ME! EAT ME! BUT NOT IMMEDIATELY.

MY CHILD IS WAITING FOR ME. I'LL GO HOME, FEED HIM AND COME BACK TO YOU.

WHAT!

HOHOHO!

DO YOU TAKE ME FOR A FOOL?

AS IF YOU'LL COME BACK, IF I LET YOU GO!

PUNYAKOTI RAN TO HER HOME AT THE FOOT OF THE HILL.

PUNYAKOTI TOLD HIM EVERYTHING ABOUT HER PROMISE TO HULIA.

MEANWHILE HULIA WAS GETTING IMPATIENT.

I SHOULDN'T HAVE LET HER GO.

SHE'LL NEVER COME...NO, THERE SHE IS!

SHE HAS KEPT HER PROMISE...EVEN THOUGH DEATH AWAITS HER HERE. WHAT A NOBLE CREATURE!

HULIA, MY BROTHER, COME! HERE I AM. EAT ME.

EAT YOU?

NEVER, MY NOBLE SISTER. NEVER.

GO BACK TO YOUR CHILD.

HULIA!

HULIA TURNED BACK AND LEFT.

AND PUNYAKOTI REJOINED HER CHILD.

14

HOW AN ELEPHANT WAS WEIGHED

Script : Shruti Desai
Illustrations : Chandrakant Rane

ONE DAY A KING SENT FOR HIS MAHOUT.

I WANT TO KNOW HOW MUCH MY ELEPHANT WEIGHS, AND IF YOU DON'T GIVE ME. THE ANSWER BY TOMORROW MORNING...

...I'LL HAVE YOU BEHEADED.

I'M DONE FOR! HOW CAN ANYONE WEIGH AN ELEPHANT? IT'S IMPOSSIBLE.

IN THOSE DAYS THEY DID NOT HAVE SCALES THAT COULD WEIGH ELEPHANTS.

AS THE MAHOUT WAS WANDERING AROUND IN DESPAIR, HE MET A SADHU

WHY DO YOU LOOK SO GLUM, MY FRIEND?

I'M IN REAL TROUBLE, SIR. THE KING HAS ASKED ME TO WEIGH HIS ELEPHANT.

IS THAT ALL? CHEER UP. GO AND BRING THE ANIMAL, ALONG WITH ONE OF YOUR FRIENDS TO THE RIVER. I'LL WAIT FOR YOU THERE.

THE MAHOUT DID AS HE WAS TOLD.

NOW GET HIM INTO THAT BOAT.

THAT'S IT. NOW MARK THE LEVEL TO WHICH THE BOAT HAS SUNK.

NOW BRING THE ELEPHANT OUT AND FILL THE BOAT WITH SAND TILL IT SINKS TO THE MARK YOU HAVE MADE.

AFTER SOME TIME —

THERE! THE BOAT HAS SUNK TO THE MARK, SIR.

DO YOU KNOW WHY? IT'S BECAUSE THE SAND YOU HAVE PUT INTO IT IS EQUAL TO THE WEIGHT OF THE ELEPHANT.

NOW WEIGH THAT SAND ON A PAIR OF SCALES AND...

I'LL KNOW THE WEIGHT OF THE ELEPHANT!

THE NEXT DAY —

DID YOU FIND OUT HOW MUCH MY ELEPHANT WEIGHS?

YES, YOUR MAJESTY.

IT WEIGHS 900 POUNDS.

THE KING REWARDED THE MAHOUT AND THE MAHOUT NEVER FORGOT THE SADHU WHO HAD SAVED HIS LIFE.

THE TWO PANDITS

ADAPTED FROM THE FOLKTALE
AS TOLD BY THE LATE SAGUNA MANJESHWAR
ILLUSTRATIONS : M. MOHANDAS

A KING INVITED TWO SCHOLARS TO HIS PALACE. ONE OF THEM WAS CALLED PANDIT GYANRAJ AND THE OTHER WAS CALLED PANDIT VIDYARAJ.

THEY WERE LEARNED MEN, AND THEY HAD SOMETHING NEW TO TELL THE KING AND HIS COURTIERS EVERY DAY.

ONE DAY—

SUCH GREAT MEN SHOULD BE GIVEN RICH REWARDS.

THE KING INVITED SEVERAL HUNDRED PEOPLE TO HIS PALACE.

WE ARE HERE TODAY TO HONOUR AND REWARD TWO OF THE MOST LEARNED MEN IN OUR LAND.

PANDIT GYANRAJ IS··· ER···

THE KING SUDDENLY FOUND THAT HE DID NOT KNOW MUCH ABOUT EITHER MAN.

PANDIT VIDYARAJ WILL BE ABLE TO HELP ME OUT.

PANDIT VIDYARAJ, PLEASE TELL ME ALL ABOUT YOUR FRIEND.

WELL... I... ER...

I MUST BE CAREFUL. IF I PRAISE GYANRAJ THE KING MIGHT GIVE HIM A BETTER REWARD THAN THE ONE HE GIVES ME.

YOUR MAJESTY, I DO NOT LIKE TO SAY IT, BUT PANDIT GYANRAJ IS AN...

...AN ASS! HE DOESN'T KNOW ANYTHING. HE JUST REPEATS WHAT HE HEARS FROM ME.

THAT'S A LIE! I HAVE HEARD PANDIT GYANRAJ SPEAK AND I KNOW HE IS LEARNED.

ANYWAY, LET'S SEE WHAT GYANRAJ HAS TO SAY ABOUT HIS FRIEND.

PANDIT GYANRAJ, PLEASE TELL ME ALL ABOUT YOUR FRIEND.

HE IS... ER...

I MUST BE CAREFUL. IF I PRAISE VIDYARAJ, THE KING MIGHT GIVE HIM A BETTER REWARD THAN THE ONE HE GIVES ME.

YOUR MAJESTY, SINCE YOU ASK ME, I MUST TELL YOU THAT PANDIT VIDYARAJ IS A...

...A DONKEY! HE DOESN'T KNOW ANYTHING. HE JUST REPEATS WHAT HE HEARS FROM ME.

THESE SCHOLARS HAVE READ MANY BOOKS BUT WHAT IS THE USE OF ALL THEIR LEARNING?

THEY ARE NO BETTER THAN ANY OF US HERE. HOW CAN I HONOUR SUCH MEN?

LISTEN CAREFULLY AND DO AS I SAY.

SOMETIME LATER TWO SERVANTS CAME IN CARRYING GIFTS.

THEY PLACED ONE PLATE BEFORE EACH PANDIT.

WHAT IS THIS, YOUR MAJESTY?

FRESH, GREEN GRASS!

YOU YOURSELVES HAVE TOLD ME THAT ONE OF YOU IS AN ASS AND THE OTHER A DONKEY.

SO I HAVE GIVEN YOU THE REWARD ASSES AND DONKEYS WOULD LIKE BEST—THE FINEST GRASS THAT COULD BE FOUND IN THE KINGDOM!

THE PANDITS FELT VERY ASHAMED OF THEMSELVES. THEY LEFT THE PALACE AND NO ONE HEARD OF THEM AGAIN.

DODDA'S DUBUKA

Illustrator: Vasant Halbe

DODDA WAS INVITED TO HIS FRIEND'S HOUSE FOR TEA.

THIS IS DELICIOUS! DELICIOUS!

PLEASE HAVE SOME MORE.

I'LL ASK MY MOTHER TO MAKE SOME AT HOME. WHAT IS IT CALLED?

KADUBU.

KADUBU... KADUBU... I MUSTN'T FORGET. KADUBU... KADUBU...

I'LL HAVE TO BE GOING NOW... KADUBU... KADUBU...

WELL DODDA, THANK YOU FOR COMING.

KADUBU... KADUBU...

KA-A-AAH!

OWW...OWW... OWW!

NOW WHAT WAS THAT SWEET CALLED?

DUBUKA!

21

THE HEAVENLY ELEPHANT   Illustrations : Ram Waeerkar

ONE DAY A LABOURER WAS LOOKING FOR WORK IN THE FIELDS WHEN HE SAW AN ELEPHANT DESCENDING FROM THE SKY.

NO ELEPHANT ON EARTH CAN FLY!

IT MUST HAVE COME FROM HEAVEN.

AFTER A WHILE—

IT'S ABOUT TO LEAVE!

I'LL GO TO HEAVEN WITH IT!

SOMETIME LATER—

AHA! HEAVEN! THERE SHOULD BE PLENTY OF WORK FOR ME HERE.

THE MAN WORKED IN HEAVEN THE REST OF THE DAY AND SPENT THE NIGHT THERE. NEXT MORNING—

NOW HOW DO I GET BACK TO EARTH?

AH, HERE COMES THE ELEPHANT!

WHEN THE MAN RETURNED HOME HE TOLD EVERYONE WHERE HE HAD BEEN.

IT'S SUCH A WONDERFUL PLACE...

...AND IT'S SUCH A JOY TO WORK THERE! THEY PAY ONE MEASURE OF RICE FOR EVERY HOUR OF WORK!

AND THEIR MEASURE IS SO LARGE!

SEE HOW MUCH RICE I GOT FOR HALF A DAY'S WORK!

AFTER HEARING HIS TALE ALL THE VILLAGERS WANTED TO GO TO HEAVEN TOO.

24

SO THE NEXT MORNING THE MAN TOOK THEM TO THE FIELD WHERE HE HAD SEEN THE ELEPHANT.

QUIET, NOW! DON'T MAKE A NOISE OR HE MAY NOT LAND HERE.

HOW MUCH DID YOU SAY THEY PAY FOR ONE HOUR'S WORK UP THERE?

ONE MEASURE OF RICE.

HOW BIG IS THE MEASURE?

THIS BIG!

QUIET! HERE HE COMES!

AS THE VILLAGERS WATCHED WITH BATED BREATH THE ELEPHANT LANDED...

...AND ATE. THEN AS IT WAS ABOUT TO LEAVE—

SOON...

...ALL THE VILLAGERS WERE FLYING UPWARD TOWARDS HEAVEN.

WE'LL STAY UP THERE AS LONG AS WE CAN!

WE'LL RETURN WITH SACKLOADS OF GRAIN!

HOW MUCH DID YOU SAY THEY PAY FOR ONE HOUR'S WORK?

ONE MEASURE OF RICE!

HOW BIG IS THE MEASURE?

THIS BIG!

THE NEXT MOMENT ALL OF THEM PLUNGED INTO A RIVER.

SPLASH

THE ELEPHANT WAS SO STARTLED BY THE NOISE THAT HE NEVER CAME TO THAT VILLAGE AGAIN.

THE MAN WHO LOVED VADAS

Illustrator: M. N. Nangre

ONE DAY KHANDOBA, THE MISER, FELT LIKE EATING VADAS.

WIFE!

YES?

WILL YOU MAKE SOME VADAS FOR ME?

I WILL, IF YOU GET ME SOME OIL AND SOME DAL.

KHANDOBA PUT ON HIS TURBAN.

YOU'LL NEED THIS TIN FOR THE OIL, WON'T YOU?

NO, I WON'T.

KHANDOBA WENT TO A SHOP IN THE MARKET.

CAN YOU SHOW ME THE BEST OIL YOU HAVE?

TRY THIS ONE, SIR.

IT'S THE BEST IN THE MARKET.

LET ME SMELL IT AND SEE.

KHANDOBA BENT FORWARD, AS IF TO SMELL THE OIL.

THE NEXT MOMENT —

OH, DEAR! MY TURBAN!

OH, NO!

AS KHANDOBA PICKED UP THE OIL-SOAKED TURBAN —

I'M EXTREMELY SORRY, SIR. YOUR TURBAN...

NEVER MIND.

GIVE IT TO ME. I'LL HAVE IT WASHED AND ...

NO, MY FRIEND. I'M IN A HURRY.

I MUST LEAVE RIGHT AWAY. I'LL COME BACK LATER FOR THE OIL.

BACK AT HOME, KHANDOBA SQUEEZED THE OIL INTO A VESSEL.

THE VESSEL IS FULL.

BUT I DON'T UNDERSTAND WHY YOU BROUGHT THE OIL IN YOUR TURBAN.

NOW TAKE THIS BAG.

WHAT FOR?

TO GET THE DAL.

I DON'T NEED YOUR BAG.

I HAVE MY TURBAN.

?

AT THE MARKET—

I WANT SOME GOOD DAL, SIR. CAN YOU SHOW ME THE BEST YOU HAVE?

HERE. HAVE A LOOK AT THE DAL IN THESE BAGS, SIR.

LET ME...OH! MY TURBAN!

:!

I'LL SEE YOU LATER.

IND KHANDOBA RETURNED HOME.

HERE YOU ARE! ALL THE DAL YOU NEED.

WHY COULDN'T YOU USE A BAG AS EVERYONE ELSE DOES?

I HAVE MY REASONS.

NOW I AM GOING OUT. I WANT THE VADAS TO BE READY BY THE TIME I RETURN.

KHANDOBA'S WIFE GROUND THE DAL, PATTED THE PASTE INTO VADAS AND BEGAN TO FRY THEM.

SOON SHE HAD A PLATEFUL OF CRISP, HOT VADAS, READY.

I THINK I'D BETTER TASTE ONE AND SEE.

But it was too late. Poor Khandoba had to go without the vadas.

RAMA TO THE RESCUE
—a folktale from Tamil Nadu

Script : Luis M. Fernandes
Illustrations : Ram Waeerkar

IN A VILLAGE, ONE NIGHT— OH-HUMM! WHAT A HARD DAY IT HAS BEEN!

I'M FEELING SO SLEEPY...

WHAT'S THE MATTER? WHAT ARE YOU LOOKING AT?

SSSSH!

LISTEN!

SOMEBODY IS TRYING TO GET IN.

I...I THINK HE HAS ALREADY GOT IN...THE NOISE HAS STOPPED.

LIE DOWN...DON'T LOOK.

IT'S A THIEF...HE MUST HAVE SOMEHOW GOT PAST RAMA.

RAMA WAS THE VILLAGE KOTWAL.

WHAT SHOULD WE DO?

I'LL TELL YOU. LISTEN...

MEANWHILE—

VOICES! THEY'RE AWAKE. I'LL HAVE TO WAIT TILL THEY FALL ASLEEP.

I WONDER WHERE THEY KEEP THEIR MONEY.

THEY'RE SAYING SOMETHING. PERHAPS THEY'RE TALKING ABOUT THEIR MONEY. I'D BETTER LISTEN CLOSELY.

WHAT SHOULD WE NAME OUR CHILD?

IF HE IS A BOY WE'LL CALL HIM RAMA.

RAMA? YES... THAT'S A GOOD NAME.

WHEN HE'S IN THE HOUSE, I'LL CALL OUT SOFTLY TO HIM. RAMA! RAMA!

RAMA, THE VILLAGE KOTWAL, RAN TO THE HOUSE FROM WHICH HE HEARD HIS NAME BEING CALLED.

OH, OH! SOME THIEF HAS DUG HIS WAY INTO THIS HOUSE.

AH, AT LAST THEY'VE STOPPED THEIR CHATTER!

NOW SOON THEY'LL GO TO SLEEP AND... EH!

YOU'RE UNDER ARREST.

IT'S RAMA! HE HEARD US!

THE PLAN WORKED! WE'RE SAVED.

THE MAN AND HIS WIFE BY THEIR CLEVERNESS HAD SAVED THEMSELVES FROM BEING ROBBED.

HOW THE MISER OUTSMARTED HIMSELF

Adapted from the folktale as told by the late Saguna Manjeshwar
Illustrations : Ram Waeerkar

ONCE UPON A TIME THERE WAS A MISERLY KING. ONE DAY A SON WAS BORN TO HIM. THIS MADE HIM VERY UNHAPPY.

NOW I'LL HAVE TO GIVE A FEAST TO THE VILLAGERS.

AND THEY EAT SO MUCH! WHAT SHOULD I DO?

AH! I HAVE AN IDEA!

AT THE FEAST EACH GUEST WAS SERVED JUST TWO LADDOOS.

IS THIS ALL WE ARE GOING TO GET?

IT'S SHAMEFUL!

GOOD PEOPLE, TODAY WE ARE GOING TO PLAY A WONDERFUL GAME. YOU MUST BE WONDERING WHY YOU HAVE BEEN SERVED JUST TWO LADDOOS.

WELL, AS SOON AS YOU FINISH THOSE TWO, YOU WILL BE SERVED ANOTHER TWO AND WHEN YOU FINISH THOSE, ANOTHER TWO AND SO ON.

BESIDES, FOR EVERY LADDOO YOU EAT YOU WILL BE PAID TWO RUPEES. BUT···

···YOU MUST EAT THE LADDOOS WITHOUT BENDING YOUR ARM AT THE ELBOW AND WITHOUT PUTTING YOUR MOUTH TO YOUR PLATE.

NOW YOU MAY START.

HOW CAN WE EAT WITHOUT BENDING OUR ARMS?

OR WITHOUT PUTTING OUR MOUTHS TO OUR PLATES?

THEY'LL HAVE TO GET UP WITHOUT EATING NOW! HEEHEE!

37

THEN SUDDENLY ONE MAN GOT AN IDEA.

I KNOW HOW WE CAN DO IT!

WHAT ARE THEY WHISPERING?

LET THEM WHISPER. THERE'S NO WAY THEY CAN EAT WITHOUT BENDING THEIR ELBOWS...

...OR WITHOUT... WHAT ARE THEY DOING!

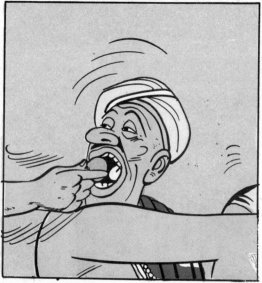

THEY'VE TRICKED ME! EACH MAN IS FEEDING HIS NEIGHBOUR!

THE GUESTS ATE AND ATE...

...MUCH TO THE DISMAY OF THEIR HOST.

STOP! STOP! DON'T EAT SO MUCH! YOU'LL GET A STOMACH-ACHE!

AT THE END OF THE FEAST EACH GUEST HAD EATEN AT LEAST FIFTY LADDOOS!

MY STOMACH IS FULL AND I HAVE EARNED A HUNDRED RUPEES.

I HAVE EARNED A HUNDRED AND TWO!

I TRIED TO SAVE MONEY AND ENDED UP PAYING OUT A FORTUNE.

WORDS FOR WORDS

Story: P. Varadarajan   Illustrations: V. B. Halbe

A CITY DWELLER WAS PASSING THROUGH A VILLAGE.

THE PEOPLE HERE ARE SO SIMPLE.

I COULD EASILY MAKE SOME MONEY HERE IF I TRIED.

LET ME BEGIN WITH THIS MAN. HE APPEARS TO BE RICH... AND FOOLISH.

OH, WHAT A NOBLE FACE YOU HAVE, SIR!

I CAN TELL THAT YOU ARE A MAN OF GREAT GENEROSITY.

WIFE, BRING TEN MEASURES OF RICE FOR MY FRIEND HERE!

RAMAN'S CAT

Illustrator: V. B. Halbe

THE EMPEROR, KRISHNA DEVA RAYA WANTED TO SEE HOW CLEVER HIS MINISTERS WERE.

CAN ANY OF YOU BRING ME A CAT...

...WHICH RUNS AWAY FROM MILK?

NO CAT WILL EVER RUN AWAY FROM MILK,

THERE'S NOTHING A CAT LIKES BETTER.

WHAT? NO ONE?

I WILL BRING YOU SUCH A CAT, YOUR MAJESTY.

THE MAN WHO SPOKE WAS RAMAN.

BUT NOT IMMEDIATELY.

THEN BRING IT WITHIN 30 DAYS

RAMAN WENT HOME AND PLACED A SAUCER OF MILK BEFORE HIS CAT.

THE CAT DIPPED ITS TONGUE INTO IT...

...AND JUMPED BACK IN ALARM. THE MILK WAS BOILING HOT!

EVERYDAY AFTER THAT RAMAN OFFERED BOILING HOT MILK TO HIS CAT...

..AND ON EACH OCCASION THE CAT BURNT ITS MOUTH WHILE TRYING TO DRINK IT.

MEOWW!

ON THE 30TH DAY RAMAN WENT TO THE PALACE.

HERE IS THE CAT, YOUR MAJESTY.

BRING A SAUCER OF MILK.

AS SOON AS THE CAT SAW THE MILK BEING BROUGHT...

...IT JUMPED OUT OF RAMAN'S ARMS...

...AND FLED IN TERROR.

YOU HAVE KEPT YOUR WORD, RAMAN. YOU ARE A VERY CLEVER MAN INDEED!

CHANDRALEKHA

Adapted from a popular folktale from Tamil Nadu

Script: Rupa Gupta
Illustrations: M.N. Nangre

ONE EVENING CHANDRALEKHA, THE FAMOUS DANCER, LOST HER WAY IN THE WOODS.

IT'S GETTING DARKER.

MUCH LATER—

OH, WHAT AM I TO DO NOW?

SUDDENLY—

VOICES!

GOOD LORD! ROBBERS!

AH! THAT WAS A GOOD DAY'S WORK!

LET'S HIDE OUR LOOT HERE. BUT BEFORE WE DO…

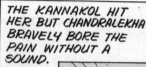

* IT IS SAID THAT A KANNAKOL OBEYS ITS MASTER'S ORDERS.

46

THE NEXT DAY WHEN THE ROBBERS RETURNED TO THE SPOT—

OUR TREASURE IS GONE!

SOMEONE MUST HAVE SEEN US BURYING IT.

IMPOSSIBLE! THE KANNAKOL WOULDN'T MISS ANYONE. BUT I'LL EXAMINE IT ANYWAY.

BLOOD! SOME ONE WAS HIT!

WE WILL FIND THE CULPRIT.

LATER—

OINTMENTS... OINTMENTS FOR ALL WOUNDS...MIRACULOUS OINTMENTS...

HE MAY HAVE SOMETHING FOR MY WOUND! RUN AND FETCH HIM.

ALL THIS MONEY IS YOURS IF YOU HAVE THE RIGHT OINTMENT FOR MY WOUND.

MY GOD! THAT WOUND ON HER ARM WAS MADE BY MY KANNAKOL.

OH-OH! IT'S THE ROBBER CHIEF! I MUST BE ON MY GUARD.

LATER THAT NIGHT—

LOOK! LOOK! SHE HAS HIDDEN THE BOXES UNDER THE BED.

LET'S TEACH HER A LESSON. COME ON, PICK UP THE BED.

YOU THINK YOU'RE VERY CLEVER MY FRIEND. BUT YOU ARE IN FOR A SURPRISE.

MUCH LATER —

THAT WITCH! SHE HAS TRICKED US!

AND LOOK WHAT'S IN THE CHEST!

STONES!

MEANWHILE CHANDRALEKHA HAD REACHED HOME...

THE ROBBERS WON'T GIVE UP SO EASILY. I MUST PREPARE MYSELF FOR ANOTHER VISIT FROM THEM.

SURE ENOUGH THEY RETURNED THE SAME NIGHT.

WELCOME, FRIENDS! I AM READY TO RECEIVE YOU.

HERE COMES THE FIRST ONE!

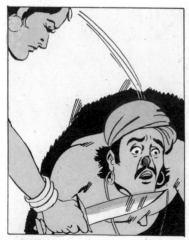

A4-EE-OH!

THE COWARD! RUNNING AWAY FROM A GIRL.

LET ME GO, CHIEF! I AM NOT AFRAID.

THE NEXT MINUTE—

A-A4-EE-OH!

SHE IS A DEVIL!

SHE HAS CUT OFF HIS NOSE!

RUN!

THEY'VE GONE, THANK GOD! AND I DON'T THINK THEY'LL DARE TO COME HERE AGAIN!

Man In The Bush

Illustrator: Bapu Patil

51

SOON—

WHAT HAPPENED?

WHAT HAPPENED?

DID HE BEAT YOU?

OH, NO! NOT AT ALL!

I POURED JUST ONE BUCKET OF WATER ON HER AND SHE STARTED SCREAMING.

THERE IS A MAN IN THAT BUSH ON WHOM I HAVE POURED TWENTY BUCKETS...

...AND HE HASN'T UTTERED A WORD! NOW...

WHERE? WHO?

COME ON, MAN! I WAS LOOKING FOR YOU.

YOU THIEF!

HOW CLEVER YOU ARE!

53

WHY THE TIGER HAS A FROWN ON HIS FACE

Illustrator: V. B. Halbe

ONCE A RABBIT WAS DOZING UNDER A TREE.

ZZ

SUDDENLY HE WOKE UP—

A TIGER!

DESPERATELY, HE LOOKED AROUND FOR HELP. THEN—

AH!

WHAT ARE YOU DOING HERE?

I AM KEEPING WATCH OVER MY GRANDFATHER'S PRECIOUS GONG.

IT IS SAID THAT HE WHO CAN SOUND IT WILL GAIN GREAT POWERS. BUT NONE OF US SMALL RABBITS CAN REACH IT!

BUT I CAN. SO I SHALL SOUND IT AND GET MORE POWER.

ALL RIGHT, BUT LET ME RUN AWAY FIRST...

WE RABBITS CAN'T BEAR THE LOUD SOUND OF THE GONG...

HA! HA! HOW CAN YOU HOPE TO GET POWER IF YOU ARE SO SCARED EVEN OF THE SOUND? RUN... RUN...

WHEN THE RABBIT WAS OUT OF SIGHT—

HEY! HEY! OW! OW! HELP!

THE TIGER, STUNG ON HIS FACE BY THE BEES, FROWNED SO HARD THAT THE MARKS BECAME PERMANENT.

THEY CAN BE SEEN TO THIS DAY EVEN ON THE FACE OF YOUNG TIGER CUBS.

NAMBI AND HIS PROTRUDING STOMACH

Illustrator: M. Mohandas

NAMBI WAS KNOWN TO EAT A LOT. ONE DAY HE WAS CALLED TO A FEAST AT THE PALACE ...

...AND THERE HE ATE SO MUCH...

...THAT THE KING AND HIS COURTIERS WERE ASTONISHED.

I'VE NEVER SEEN A MAN WITH A GREATER APPETITE.

BRING MORE RICE AND SWEETS. SERVE HIM WELL. HE IS MY SPECIAL GUEST.

MAHARAJ, YOU ARE A KIND HOST.

AN HOUR LATER —

HOW WAS THE FOOD?

EXCELLENT, YOUR HIGHNESS. I AM SO FULL, I COULD NOT EAT A SPOON-FUL MORE.

BUT WE HAVE NOT YET SERVED YOU 'PALAPAYASAM'*, THE KING OF SWEETS. WILL YOU REFUSE IT?

HOW CAN I REFUSE ANYTHING YOU OFFER, O KING?

NAMBI THEN GULPED TWO LITRES OF PALAPAYASAM...

HOW DOES HE DO IT?

YOU CAN GIVE ME SOME MORE.

HE'LL SURELY BURST!

ADMIRABLE, NAMBI! BUT HOW COULD YOU EAT SO MUCH PALAPAYASAM AFTER YOU SAID THERE WAS NO SPACE FOR EVEN A SPOONFUL OF FOOD?

YOUR HIGHNESS, IN A CROWDED STREET, PEOPLE MOVE ASIDE TO LET YOU PASS...

...IN THE SAME WAY, WHEN PALAPAYASAM, THE KING OF SWEETS ARRIVED, ALL THE OTHER FOOD IN MY STOMACH MADE WAY FOR IT!

HA! HA! WELL SAID!

AND FROM THAT DAY ON, NAMBI BECAME ONE OF THE KING'S FAVOURITES!

* A SWEET DISH

The Dwarf Who Outwitted the Giant

Illustrations: Ram Waeerkar

Based on a story sent by Praveen Murthy.

I AM JUST AS STRONG AND SMART AS YOU.

HA HA! THAT'S THE FUNNIEST THING I'VE EVER HEARD.

ANYWAY, YOU'VE COME JUST IN TIME. I'M HUNGRY.

WAIT A MINUTE, SIR.

YOU-YOU CAN'T POSSIBLY WANT TO EAT ME! I'M AFTER ALL, SO VERY SMALL!

I'LL LOOK FOR MORE FOOD AFTERWARDS.

WAIT!

I HAVE A CHALLENGE FOR YOU!

A CHALLENGE? FOR ME? FROM YOU?

WHAT SORT OF CHALLENGE?

PUT ME DOWN FIRST.

THERE!

The Priest's Assistant
An Indian Folktale

Script : Gayatri M Dutt
Illustrations : Ashok Dongre

A POOR PRIEST WAS ONCE CALLED TO A WEALTHY MAN'S HOUSE TO PERFORM A CEREMONY.

WIFE, I AM INDEED FORTUNATE!

THIS RICH MAN IS SURE TO PAY ME HANDSOMELY!

AT LEAST, I HOPE HE DOES.

WHY NOT SEND OUR SON IN ADVANCE, AS YOUR ASSISTANT...

A GOOD IDEA! IF THE RICH MAN THINKS I'M IMPORTANT ENOUGH TO HAVE AN ASSISTANT...

... HE MIGHT PAY ME MORE.

JUST THEN, THEIR SON CAME IN. THE PRIEST'S WIFE TOOK HER HUSBAND ASIDE —

YOU KNOW HOW FOOLISH OUR SON IS. YOU'D BETTER TELL HIM EXACTLY WHAT HE SHOULD DO.

61

SO THE PRIEST EXPLAINED HIS PLAN TO HIS SON. THEN—

...BUT, MIND YOU, UNLIKE US THESE PEOPLE ARE RICH. THERE WILL BE CHAIRS AND TABLES AT THEIR HOUSE...

...SO BE SURE NOT TO SIT ON THE FLOOR. SIT ON A CHAIR, DO YOU HEAR?

SIT ON A CHAIR... A HIGH SEAT... A SEAT THAT IS HIGHER THAN THE GROUND. DO YOU UNDERSTAND?

OH, YES, YES, CERTAINLY!

AND TALK SENSIBLY AND ON IMPORTANT MATTERS.

WHAT?

HELP ME, GOD!

I SAID, TALK ON SERIOUS TOPICS... WEIGHTY MATTERS. DOES THAT MAKE SENSE TO YOU?

WEIGHTY MATTERS? FINE, FINE! DON'T WORRY.

SO WITH HIS FATHER'S ADVICE IN MIND, THE YOUTH SET OFF AND SOON ARRIVED AT THE RICH MAN'S HOUSE.

HE MUST BE THE PRIEST'S ASSISTANT.

HE WAS GIVEN A WARM WELCOME—

COME, PLEASE TAKE A SEAT.

SHE'S OFFERING ME A MAT TO SIT ON. BUT FATHER SAID...

THE YOUNG PRIEST LOOKED THIS WAY AND THAT...

...AND THEN MADE STRAIGHT FOR THE COW-SHED IN THE COURTYARD.

DONE IT! AND NOW I MUST TALK ABOUT HEAVY THINGS!

ER... WHAT ARE YOU DOING UP THERE? PLEASE COME DOWN.

HAMMER-HEAD.

WHAT?

WHY MUST YOU SIT THERE? COME INTO THE HOUSE.

AXE HEAD

?

I DON'T UNDERSTAND. PLEASE COME INSIDE.

GRINDING STONE.

HE'S GONE MAD!!

JUST THEN, THE PRIEST ARRIVED. WHEN HE HEARD WHAT HAD HAPPENED, HE FLUSHED WITH EMBARRASSMENT.

ME AND MY GRAND IDEAS!

AND GOING INTO THE COW-SHED, HE STERNLY ORDERED HIS SON TO COME DOWN!

A Bowl of Rice

Script: Rajani Thindiath
Illustrator: Arijit Dutta Chowdhury
Colourist: Umesh Sarode

MANI WAS A POOR MAN. HE WORKED HARD...

...BUT BARELY MANAGED TO MAKE A LIVING –

HERE'S 10 RUPEES... THAT IS ALL I MANAGED TO EARN TODAY. THE ROAD IS COMPLETE... THERE'S NO MORE WORK TILL NEXT SUMMER!

I'LL GO TO THE TOWN TOMORROW. I MIGHT FIND SOME WORK THERE.

EARLY NEXT MORNING, MANI WRAPPED A HANDFUL OF RICE IN A PIECE OF CLOTH, AND SET OUT –

TOWARDS NOON –

IT'S HOT! I'LL REST FOR A WHILE UNDER THE COOL SHADE OF THIS BANYAN TREE.

ZZZZZZZZZ....

UNKNOWN TO MANI, THE BANYAN TREE WAS THE ABODE OF WOOD SPIRITS –

THERE'S A MAN SLEEPING UNDER OUR TREE!

AND HE HAS TIED HIS LUNCH TO THAT BRANCH!

SMELLS LIKE STALE RICE!

IT HAS BEEN AGES SINCE I'VE HAD RICE!

LET'S TAKE IT!

THIS IS YUMMY! WHAT A CHANGE FROM OUR DAILY DIET OF NECTAR AND FRUITS!

THE STALENESS ADDS TO ITS FLAVOUR!

THAT WAS ONE OF THE MOST SATIS-FYING MEALS IN A LONG TIME!

HMMM... WE OWE IT TO THE MAN SLEEPING BELOW.

LET'S LEAVE HIM SOMETHING IN EXCHANGE!

SOMETIME LATER WHEN MANI AWOKE –

?!

67

ONCE HOME, HE TOLD HIS WIFE ALL THAT HAD HAPPENED –

THE GODS HAVE SMILED ON US! LET'S INVITE ALL THE VILLAGERS TO A FEAST!

GOOD IDEA!

SO MANI WENT FROM DOOR TO DOOR INVITING EVERY-ONE IN THE VILLAGE –

MY WIFE AND I ARE HOLDING A FEAST AT OUR HOME, TOMORROW. PLEASE COME!

A FEAST! AT POOR MANI'S HOUSE! HA! HA! HA!

WE'RE SURE TO COME BACK WITH EMPTY STOMACHS! BETTER HAVE A HEARTY LUNCH BEFORE GOING!

ON THE DAY OF THE FEAST–

ONLY FOUR BOWLS!

AND SUCH SMALL ONES AT THAT!

O DIVINE MAIDENS, COME FORTH AND SHARE YOUR BOUNTY!

THE MOUTH-WATERING DISHES KEPT ON COMING –

I'VE NEVER HAD SUCH A FEAST IN MY LIFE!

AH! I AM SO FULL... I GUESS I WILL HAVE TO ROLL MYSELF HOME!

THE NEWS OF THE FEAST SPREAD LIKE WILDFIRE TILL IT REACHED THE EARS OF MUTHURAMAN, THE RICHEST MAN IN THE VILLAGE –

MAGIC BOWLS! I WONDER HOW THAT WRETCH GOT HOLD OF SUCH WONDROUS THINGS! I HAVE TO FIND OUT!

MANI, OH, MANI!

IT'S MUTHURAMAN! INVITE HIM FOR LUNCH.

MUTHURAMAN WAS TREATED TO A DELICIOUS LUNCH. AFTERWARDS –

SO TELL ME, MANI. HOW DID YOU GET THE MAGIC BOWLS?

OH! THE WOOD SPIRITS GAVE THEM TO ME IN RETURN FOR A HANDFUL OF RICE!

A HANDFUL OF RICE! I CAN DO MUCH BETTER!

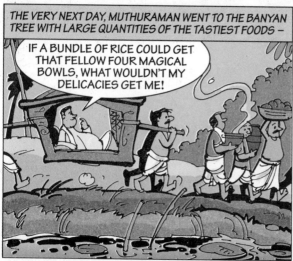

THE VERY NEXT DAY, MUTHURAMAN WENT TO THE BANYAN TREE WITH LARGE QUANTITIES OF THE TASTIEST FOODS –

IF A BUNDLE OF RICE COULD GET THAT FELLOW FOUR MAGICAL BOWLS, WHAT WOULDN'T MY DELICACIES GET ME!

YOU MAY LEAVE NOW. COME TO COLLECT ME IN THE EVENING.

NOW I'LL PRETEND TO SLEEP AND WATCH OUT FOR THE WOOD SPIRITS!

BUT MUTHURAMAN FELL ASLEEP AND WHEN HE WOKE UP –

OH I MISSED SEEING THE WOOD SPIRITS! BUT THE FOOD... IT HAS DISAPPEARED!

AH! AND HERE ARE THE FOUR BOWLS... THOUGH THEY DO HAVE ODD SHAPES!

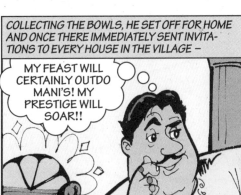

COLLECTING THE BOWLS, HE SET OFF FOR HOME AND ONCE THERE IMMEDIATELY SENT INVITATIONS TO EVERY HOUSE IN THE VILLAGE –

MY FEAST WILL CERTAINLY OUTDO MANI'S! MY PRESTIGE WILL SOAR!!

ON THE DAY OF THE FEAST –

IF MANI COULD GIVE US SUCH A WONDERFUL FEAST JUST IMAGINE HOW MUCH BETTER MUTHURAMAN'S WILL BE!

I'M PLANNING TO GORGE MYSELF. IN FACT I HAVEN'T EATEN A SINGLE THING TODAY!

IS EVERYBODY HERE? SHALL WE START?

I PROMISE YOU, YOU WILL NEVER FORGET THIS FEAST!

MAGIC BOWLS! COME FORTH AND SERVE MY GUESTS IN A MANNER BEFITTING MY STATUS!

THUD!

ULP!

WHAT'S THIS? THEY HAVE NO FOOD!

INSTEAD THEY HAVE… HAVE… RAZORS!

WE'RE BARBERS AND WE SHAVE THE HEADS OF ANYONE WHO CALLS US!

NO! NO, PLEASE!

71

EACH AND EVERY VILLAGER WAS SEIZED AND HIS HEAD SHAVED UNTIL IT GLEAMED. ONLY MANI WAS SPARED –

AAAH!

OH NO! OH PLEASE! SPARE ME!

FIE ON YOU, MUTHURAMAN! IS THIS THE TREATMENT YOU METE OUT TO YOUR GUESTS!

MANI, FED US GENEROUSLY AND WELL, WHILE YOU...

...HUMILIATED US!

AS MUTHURAMAN HAD PROMISED, THE VILLAGERS NEVER FORGOT THE 'FEAST' HE GAVE THEM!